The Lion's Tail

SCOTT, FORESMAN AND COMPANY • GLENVIEW, ILLINOIS
Dallas, Tex. • Oakland, N.J. • Palo Alto, Cal. • Tucker, Ga. • Brighton, England

ISBN 0-673-10608-X

Once upon a time a lion couldn't
find his tail.

He was very sad.

A mouse came along.

4

The mouse looked in front of the lion.

The mouse looked behind the lion.

But he couldn't find the lion's tail.

A monkey came along.

The monkey looked in front of the lion.

The monkey looked behind the lion.

But he couldn't find the lion's tail.

A turtle came along.

The turtle looked in front of the lion.

The turtle looked behind the lion.

I bet I can find your tail.

Get up, Mr. Lion.

The lion got up.

Who looked for the lion's tail?

the mouse   the turtle   the bee

Who found the lion's tail?

the turtle   the fish   the monkey

27 28 29 30 31 32 RRD 090807